Baseball ABC

McLoughlin Bros

Alpha Editions

This edition published in 2021

ISBN : 9789354592492

Design and Setting By
Alpha Editions
www.alphaedis.com
Email - info@alphaedis.com

BASEBALL

ABC

A B C D E F
G H I J K L
M N O P Q
R S T U V
W X Y Z

a b c d e f g
h i j k l m n
o p q r s t u
v w x y z

A B C D E F

G H I J K L

M N O P Q

R S T U V

W X Y Z

a b c d e f g

h i j k l m n

o p q r s t u

v w x y z

A stands for ARTHUR, a boy fond of fun,
When Base-Ball he plays, none like him can run.

B stands for BALL, for BAT, and for BASE.

C stands for CATCHER, with mask on his face.

D stands for DIAMOND drawn flat on the ground.

E stands for EDWARD, who marks out the bound.

F stands for FOUL on which Arthur goes out.

G stands for "GO"—How the merry boys shout!

H stands for HIGH-BALL, knocked up to the sky.

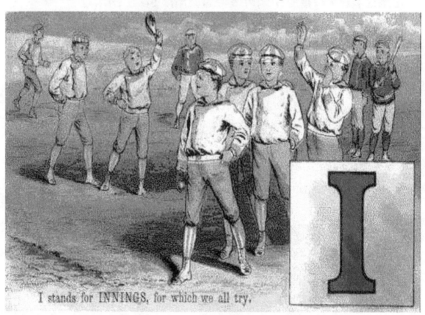

I stands for INNINGS, for which we all try.

J stands for "JUDGEMENT," the Base-Keeper's shout.

J stands for "JUDGEMENT," the Base-Keeper's shout.

K stands for KARL who so quickly gets out.

K stands for KARL who so quickly gets out.

L stands for LEFT-FIELD, who catches FLY-BALLS.

L stands for LEFT-FIELD, who catches FLY-BALLS.

M stands for MUFF, who cannot catch at all.

M stands for MUFF, who cannot catch at all.

N stands for NORMAN, who knocks the ball high.

O stands for OUT, when it's caught on the fly.

P stands for PITCHER, a smart boy you see.

Q stands for QUICK, which this pitcher must be.

R stands for RUNNER, who runs to each base.

R stands for RUNNER, who runs to each base.

S stands for SHORT-STOP, the ball he must chase.

S stands for SHORT-STOP, the ball he must chase.

T stands for THIRD-BASE, looked after by James.

U stands for UMPIRE, who judges these games.

V stands for VICTOR, the best of the nine.

W stands for WILLIAM, who tells us the time.

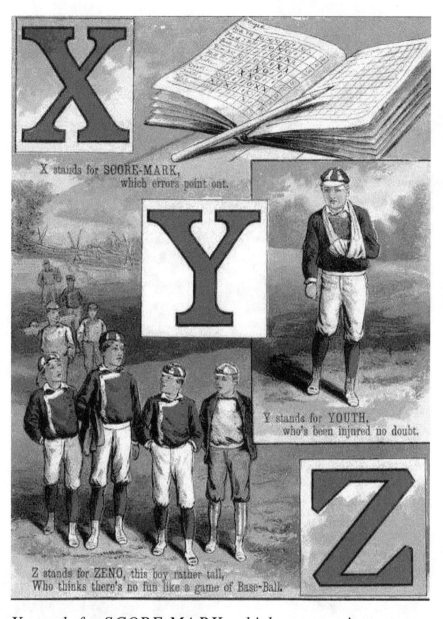

X stands for SCORE-MARK, which errors point out.

Y stands for YOUTH, who's been injured no doubt.

Z stands for ZENO, this boy rather tall,
Who thinks there's no fun like a game of Base-Ball.

BASE-BALL A. B. C.

A stands for ARTHUR, a boy fond of fun,
When Base-Ball he plays, none like him can run.
B stands for BALL, for BAT, and for BASE.
C stands for CATCHER, with mask on his face.
D stands for DIAMOND drawn flat on the ground.
E stands for EDWARD, who marks out the bound.
F stands for FOUL on which Arthur goes out.
G stands for "Go"—How the merry boys shout!
H stands for HIGH-BALL, knocked up to the sky.
I stands for INNINGS, for which we all try.
J stands for JUDGMENT, the Base-Keeper's shout.
K stands for KARL, who so quickly gets out.
L stands for LEFT-FIELD, who catches FLY-BALLS.
M stands for MUFF, who cannot catch at all.
N stands for NORMAN, who knocks the ball high.
O stands for OUT, when it's caught on the fly.
P stands for PITCHER, a smart boy you see.
Q stands for QUICK, which this pitcher must be.
R stands for RUNNER, who runs to each base.
S stands for SHORT-STOP, the ball he must chase.
T stands for THIRD-BASE, looked after by James.
U stands for UMPIRE, who judges these games.
V stands for VICTOR, the best of the nine.
W stands for WILLIAM, who tells us the time.
X stands for SCORE-MARK, which errors point out.
Y stands for YOUTH, who's been injured no doubt.
Z stands for ZENO, this boy rather tall,
Who thinks there's no fun like a game of Base-Ball.

BASE-BALL A. B. C.

A   *stands for ARTHUR, a boy fond of fun,*

When Base-Ball he plays, none like him can run.

B   *stands for BALL, for BAT, and for BASE.*

C   *stands for CATCHER, with mask on his face.*

D   *stands for DIAMOND drawn flat on the ground.*

E   *stands for EDWARD, who marks out the bound.*

F   *stands for FOUL on which Arthur goes out.*

G   *stands for "GO"—How the merry boys shout!*

H	*stands for HIGH-BALL, knocked up to the sky.*
I	*stands for INNINGS, for which we all try.*
J	*stands for JUDGEMENT, the Base-Keeper's shout.*
K	*stands for KARL, who so quickly gets out.*
L	*stands for LEFT-FIELD, who catches FLY-BALLS.*
M	*stands for MUFF, who cannot catch at all.*
N	*stands for NORMAN, who knocks the ball high.*
O	*stands for OUT, when it's caught on the fly.*
P	*stands for PITCHER, a smart boy you see.*

Q	*stands for QUICK, which this pitcher must be.*
R	*stands for RUNNER, who runs to each base.*
S	*stands for SHORT-STOP, the ball he must chase.*
T	*stands for THIRD-BASE, looked after by James.*
U	*stands for UMPIRE, who judges these games.*
V	*stands for VICTOR, the best of the nine.*
W	*stands for WILLIAM, who tells us the time.*
X	*stands for SCORE-MARK, which errors point out.*
Y	*stands for YOUTH, who's been injured no doubt.*

Z   *stands for ZENO, this boy rather tall,*

Who thinks there's no fun like a game of Base-Ball.

CPSIA information can be obtained
at www.ICGtesting.com
Printed in the USA
LVHW030916020721
691544LV00009B/599